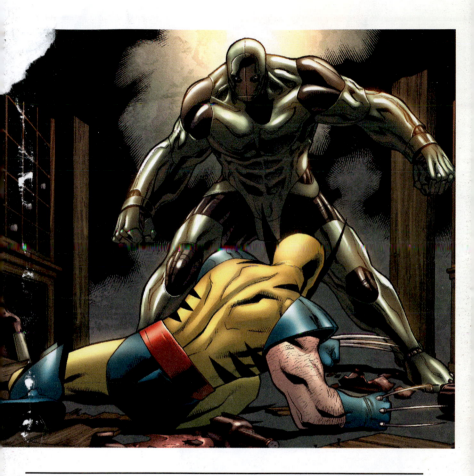

WOLVERINE: FIRST CLASS

THE ROOKIE

FRED VAN LENTE ▪ ANDREA DI VITO ▪ SALVA ESPIN
CLAYTON HENRY ▪ STEVEN CUMMINGS

WOLVERINE: FIRST CLASS

THE ROOKIE

CONTENTS

MARVEL *POCKET BOOK*   Wolverine: First Class - The Rookie

Wolverine: First Class - The Rookie. Marvel Pocketbook Vol. 1. Contains material originally published in magazine form as Wolverine: First Class 1-8. First printing 2009. Published by Panini Publishing, a division of Panini UK Limited. Mike Riddell, Managing Director. Alan O'Keefe, Managing Editor. Mark Irvine, Production Manager. Marco M. Lupoi, Publishing Director Europe. Ed Hammond, Reprint Editor. Darren Miles, Designer. Office of publication: Brockbourne House, 77 Mount Ephraim, Tunbridge Wells. Kent TN4 8BS. MARVEL, Wolverine, X-Men and all related characters and the distinctive likenesses thereof are trademarks of Marvel Entertainment, Inc. and its subsidiaries, and are used with permission. Copyright © 2008 & 2009 Marvel Entertainment, Inc. and its subsidiaries. No similarity between any of the names, characters, persons and/or institutions in this edition with those of any living or dead person or institution is intended, and any such similarity which may exist is purely coincidental. This publication may not be sold, except by authorised dealers, and is sold subject to the condition that it shall not be sold or distributed with any part of its cover or markings removed, nor in a mutilated condition. This publication is produced under licence from Marvel Characters B.V. through Panini S.p.A. Printed in Italy. www.marvel.com. All rights reserved. ISBN: 978-1-84653-082-1

August 20.

Dear Diary,
Big day today. Lots of *firsts*.

First time I finally got my *dorm room* to look the way I really *wanted* it to.

KITTY! *KITTY PRYDE!*

First inkling I might have a *crush* on the *boy next door.**

COME DOWN! WE'RE *PICKING TEAMS* AND I WANT YOU TO BE ON *MINE!*

OKAY, PETER! I'M ON MY WAY!

*I mean that *literally*--He's in the room *right next* to me. HOW AM I GONNA SLEEP AT NIGHT?!?!? *AAAAHHH!!*

My first day of *classes*...

...at the *Xavier School for Gifted Youngsters*.

Prof. X takes them *in*, teaches them how to use their powers *safely*...

WITH *FIVE PLAYERS*, IT'S THE ONLY WAY TO HAVE SAME-SIZE *TEAMS*...

...ALTHOUGH IF THE *SIXTH* X-MAN AGREED TO PLAY, IT WOULDN'T BE A *PROBLEM*...

...and shows a world which fears and *mistrusts* mutants that Homo superior can be *heroes*...

I *GOT* I—

OOF!

SORRY-- I'M SUCH A-- WHAT'S THE WORD IN *ENGLISH?*

KLUTZ?

Y-YES... "*KLUTZ*" IS THE WORD...

BONK

...by sending his students out to battle evil as the X-Men.

WOLVERINE!

Wolverine is the *one* X-Man I don't quite get.

CAN YOU GET THE *BALL?*

His mutant power is that he can heal from *any injury*--

--a power that allowed *surgery* that laced his bones with an unbreakable metal, *Adamantium*...

...and gave him *claws* made of the same material.

THERE.

IT'S *GOT.*

SNIKT

POP

FEEEEEEEEEEE

No one knows who *did* that to him...

...not even *him*. His memory's pretty *iffy*.

GEE.

THANKS.

I didn't realize *amnesia* made you so *cranky*.

[9]

NO... ...I'D LIKE YOU TO BRING *KITTY*.

WHAT?!

ME?

HER?

BUT--SHE HASN'T GONE ON A SINGLE *MISSION* YET!

THAT WOULD BE THE *IDEA*. IT HAS BEEN *SOME TIME* SINCE I ACCEPTED MY *FIRST CLASS* OF X-MEN.

BACK THEN, I TAUGHT ALL THEIR CLASSES *MYSELF*, BUT THOSE STUDENTS WERE ALL RELATIVELY *YOUNG*.

YOU *NEW* X-MEN ARE MUCH *OLDER*, MORE *EXPERIENCED*. I THINK OUR *YOUNGER* STUDENTS, LIKE KITTY, SHOULD GAIN THE *BENEFIT* OF THAT.

CALL IT...AN *INTERNSHIP*, IF YOU WILL.

AN *INTERN*--? YOUR *WHEELS* SCREWED ON TOO TIGHT, CHARLIE? I DON'T KNOW IF YOU *NOTICED*, BUT I'M NOT EXACTLY THE NURTURING *TYPE*.

THE WAY *I* OPERATE, A NEWBIE IS JUST GOING TO HOLD ME *BACK*-- OR *WORSE*. NO. *FORGET* IT.

WHY DON'T YOU STICK HER WITH *STORM*-- OR THE *ELF*--

BECAUSE I HAVE CHOSEN *YOU*.

AND IF YOU *DON'T* DO IT, I, IN TURN, WILL FEEL MUCH *LESS* INCLINED...

...TO CONTINUE PROBING YOUR *MIND* FOR YOUR LOST *MEMORIES*.

WE AIN'T HAD OUR *LAST WORDS* ABOUT THIS, CHARLIE.

CHARLES.

WHATEVER.

First trip in the X-Men's *Blackbird* jet.

First time I put on my X-Men *costume*...

GEEZ. THIS REALLY *ITCHES*...AND IT SMELLS LIKE *NEW CAR SEAT*...

SAY...CAN I...ASK YOU A *QUESTION*?

GRUNT

I...HAVE THIS *FRIEND*. SHE THINKS PETER--*COLOSSUS*--MIGHT BE KIND OF...*CUTE.*

WHAT DO YOU *KNOW* ABOUT HIM?

HE'S *RUSSIAN.*

HIS SKIN CAN TURN INTO *METAL.*

OH. O-*KAY*... YOU MIND IF I TURN ON SOME *MUSI*--

YES.

HEY, WHAT *CODE NAME* DO YOU THINK I SHOULD USE?

I CAN'T DECIDE BETWEEN *"PHASE"* AND *"PHANTOM GIRL"*--

WHAT ABOUT *"MUTE GIRL?"*

I still can't believe something so *big* can land with barely a *whisper*.

I'M LOCKING YOU IN FROM THE *OUTSIDE.*

WHEN AND *IF* I MAKE IT BACK, YOU'LL KNOW IT'S ME BY TWO *SHORT* KNOCKS, FOLLOWED BY ONE--

WHAT? PROFESSOR XAVIER SAID YOU HAD TO TAKE ME *WITH* YOU!

YEAH, BUT I DON'T SEE HIM *AROUND* HERE ANYWHERE, DO YOU?

LOOK. YOU SEEM LIKE A *NICE* KID.

THAT'S TOO BAD. *NICE* KIDS SHOULDN'T COME WITHIN A *TEN-MILE RADIUS* OF A GUY LIKE ME.

I GOT NOTHING TO *TEACH* YOU BECAUSE I WOULDN'T WISH WHAT'S INSIDE MY HEAD ON MY *WORST* ENEMY.

THE THINGS I'VE SEEN...AND *DONE*...

...NICE KIDS SHOULDN'T HAVE TO LEARN *ANY* OF THAT.

This girl--clearly a *mutant*-- didn't look like she lived in a town filled with *prejudice*.

In fact, it looked like this tiny town completely *embraced* her strangeness, in a way tiny towns sometimes *do*.

So what *happened*? What *changed*?

How could everything have gone so horribly *wrong* so horribly *fast*...

...unless...

...unless the town isn't the *problem*.

WOLVERINE! *STOP!* I KNOW WHAT'S *HAPPENING!*

YOU HAVE TO--

RAAAAHH!

THE *MUTANT* WE WERE SENT HERE TO FIND--*SHE'S* CAUSING ALL THIS--

SKREEEENCH

I-I'VE BEEN TO HER *HOUSE*-- LOOK, I GOT HER *SWEATER!* YOU CAN GET HER *SCENT* OFF IT--

--TRACK HER DOWN WITH YOUR *ENHANCED SENSES!*

I *KNOW* YOU CAN DO IT, WOLVERINE!

Though you could say *I* had something to do with it...

...I think, really, the beast *inside* Wolverine got under control...

...by the *hero* within *him.*

≷PANT≷

≷PANT≷

OKAY, KID...

GIVE IT *HERE.*

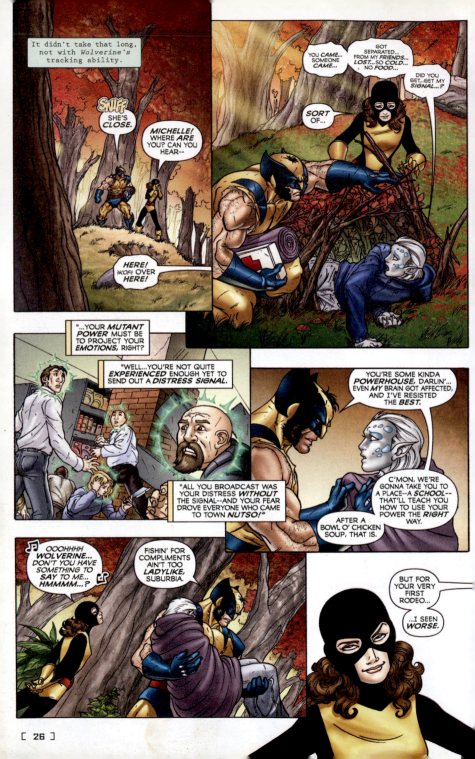

It didn't take that long, not with *Wolverine's* tracking ability.

SNIFF SHE'S *CLOSE.*

MICHELLE! WHERE *ARE* YOU? CAN YOU *HEAR--*

HERE! *KOF* OVER *HERE!*

YOU *CAME...* SOMEONE *CAME...*

GOT *SEPARATED...* FROM MY *FRIENDS... LOST...*SO *COLD...* NO *FOOD...*

SORT OF...

DID YOU *GET...GET* MY *SIGNAL...?*

"...YOUR *MUTANT POWER* MUST BE TO PROJECT YOUR *EMOTIONS,* RIGHT?

"WELL...YOU'RE NOT QUITE *EXPERIENCED* ENOUGH YET TO SEND OUT A *DISTRESS SIGNAL.*

"ALL YOU BROADCAST WAS YOUR *DISTRESS WITHOUT* THE SIGNAL--AND YOUR *FEAR* DROVE EVERYONE WHO CAME TO TOWN *NUTSO!"*

YOU'RE SOME KINDA *POWERHOUSE,* DARLIN'... EVEN *MY* BRAIN GOT AFFECTED, AND I'VE RESISTED THE *BEST.*

C'MON, WE'RE GONNA TAKE YOU TO A PLACE--A *SCHOOL--* THAT'LL TEACH YOU HOW TO USE YOUR POWER THE *RIGHT* WAY.

AFTER A BOWL O' CHICKEN SOUP, THAT IS.

♪♫ OOOHHHH *WOLVERINE...* DON'T YOU HAVE SOMETHING TO *SAY* TO ME... HMMMM...? ♫

FISHIN' FOR COMPLIMENTS AIN'T TOO *LADYLIKE,* SUBURBIA.

BUT FOR YOUR VERY FIRST RODEO...

...I SEEN *WORSE.*

But as soon as we got back...

YOU REALLY *CROSSED THE LINE* THIS TIME, XAVIER!

?!?

YOU *KNEW* THAT NEW MUTANT'S POWER WAS TO PUMP UP *EMOTIONS*--

--SHE COULDA SENT ME OFF ON ONE O' MY *ANIMAL RAGES*--

--AND YOU LET THE PRYDE GIRL COME ALONG *ANYWAY?!* YOU KNOW WHAT I COULDA *DONE* TO HER?!

PERHAPS I BELIEVED THE *RISK* WAS FAR OUTWEIGHED...

...BY WHAT *SHE* COULD DO FOR *YOU.*

DO NOT FORGET I HAVE LOOKED INTO YOUR MIND *MANY* A TIME, WOLVERINE...

...AND FOUND THERE A *BIGGER* THREAT THAN YOUR *"ANIMAL RAGES"*...

...AND THAT IS YOUR FEAR *OF* THEM, I *KNOW* THAT'S WHY YOU REFUSE TO GET *CLOSE* TO ANY OF THE OTHER X-MEN--

GIVE THE STRAY A *PUPPY* TO *TAME* HIM? *THAT* THE IDEA?

THIS MANSION IS STILL A *SCHOOL,* AND I CONSIDER ALL THOSE WHO LIVE UNDER ITS ROOF *STUDENTS.*

EVEN *YOU* STILL HAVE SOMETHING TO *LEARN.* IF NOT FROM ME...

...THEN, PERHAPS, FROM *KITTY.*

OKAY, CHARLIE, OKAY. YOU WIN.

IT'S *POSSIBLE* YOU'RE NOT AS DUMB AS YOU *LOOK.*

Like I said, a day of *firsts*.

The *main* one being...

KITTY! KITTY PRYDE!

C'MON DOWN!

WHY? ANOTHER VOLLEYBALL GAME?

NAH, I'M NOT MUCH OF A *TEAM PLAYER*.

I JUST BOUGHT A USED *MOTORCROSS* BIKE OUT OF THE LOCAL PENNYSAVER.

WANT ME TO SHOW YOU HOW TO POP *WHEELIES* WITHOUT A *HELMET*?

...this is the *first* time I feel like I really *belong* here.

DO I?!

And you know what the *funny* thing is?

I don't think I'm the *only* one.

love, Kitty

"THE BUDDY SYSTEM"

was brought to you by

FRED VAN LENTE *and* ANDREA DI VITO
WRITER   ARTIST

LAURA VILLARI COLORIST   SIMON BOWLAND LETTERER   SALVA ESPIN & BRAD ANDERSON COVER
JOE SABINO PRODUCTION   NATHAN COSBY ASSISTANT EDITOR   MARK PANICCIA EDITOR
JOE QUESADA EDITOR IN CHIEF   DAN BUCKLEY PUBLISHER

I've lost the first *battle*.

But I *will* win the *war!*

For *Dazzler!*

It's times like *these* I'm glad I stay up all night cracking Professor Xavier's *computer encryptions*.

The data Prof. X has gotten out of Wolverine's brain during all their *mind-probe sessions* must be able to give me *some* clue how I can get on his *good* side...

...if he *has* a good side...

Wait...

Really?!

If this is *true*...

...it's *perfect!*

SOON **ANOTHER** OF MY **DARK BRETHREN** SHALL STALK OUT OF THE SHADOWS...

...TO TAKE YOUR **DRINK ORDERS!**

THANK YOU...

‹LOGAN, DARLING, WHAT'S THE **MATTER?** YOU'VE BEEN SO...**AGITATED,** EVER SINCE YOUR **PARTY** STARTED.›

‹ARE YOU-- ARE YOU NOT **HAPPY** TO **SEE ME...?**›

‹NAW, IT'S NOT **THAT** BABE--**NEVER** THAT.›

‹IT'S JUST...THE **KID** DOESN'T KNOW WHAT SHE'S GOTTEN US **INTO,** HERE. I'M GONNA HAVE TO SHOVE **OFF** BEFORE IT GETS TOO MUCH **LATER.**›

‹I'M...**ASHAMED.** I DIDN'T WANT ANYONE TO **KNOW.** USUALLY, FOR MY **BIRTHDAY,** I SNEAK OFF, TO SOME **ISOLATED PLACE...**›

‹...BECAUSE... EVERY **YEAR,** WITHOUT **FAIL...**›

SNIFF SNIFF

BWOMFF

HOWDY! I'M **CAITLIN-SAN!** WELCOME TO **NINJA DOJO!**

WOULD Y'ALL LIKE TO HEAR ABOUT OUR JUICY **CHICKEN TERIYAKI STICKS?**

ER...NO, WE'LL STILL NEED A FEW MINUTES...

OKEY-DOKE!

YAAAHH!

SNIKT

BEE BEE

‹BLAST... THIS IS **TOKYO.** I'M SO SORRY, LOGAN, I **HAVE** TO TAKE THIS.›

BEE BEE

‹BUT WHEN I COME **BACK,** I WANT YOU TO TELL ME **EXACTLY** WHAT IT IS THAT'S **TROUBLING** YOU...›

SNIFF

38]

SHERAKK

THIS *SHARP* ENOUGH FOR YOU?

TCH. YOU AIN'T ANSWERED MY *QUESTION* YET, BOY.

WHICH *HER* DO YOU WANT ME TO LEAVE *OUT* OF IT?

KITTY!

IF SHE'S STILL IN THE CASTLE, I'LL *FIND* HER--

NOT SO *FAST,* BUCKO--

SNIFF SNIFF

THAT'D BE *CHEATIN'!*

AND I DON'T JUST *MAKE* THE RULES AROUND HERE--

GAAGGH!

--I *ENFORCE* 'EM!

Well, *this* is embarrassing.

WHAAA...?

I don't even remember getting *knocked out*--

SOMEBODY CALL 9-1-1!

I *DID!* THE COPS ARE ON THEIR WAY--

WHAT'S WRONG?

GET *OUTTA* HERE, KID! THESE TWO PSYCHO *REDNECKS*--

"--THEY'RE *TRASHING* THE *KITCHEN!*"

WHICH *ONE,* BOY? THE *GIRL* OR THE *WOMAN?*

WHACK

KRASH

NOW, THE *JAPANESE* BROAD--SHE'S THE LOVE OF YOUR *LIFE!*

THAT'D BE TOUGH TO LOSE.

BUT THE *YOUNG'UN--*

--SHE'S LIKE YOUR *INTERN* OR SOMETHING, RIGHT? YOUR *RESPONSIBILITY!*

SsssssS

DAZZLER!!

DAZZLER!!

DAZZLER!!

I WONDER IF I COULD POP MY *CLAWS* THROUGH MY SKULL SO FAST MY HEALING FACTOR COULDN'T SAVE ME?

"SURPRISE!!"

was brought to you by...

FRED **VAN LENTE** – WRITER
ANDREA **DI VITO** – ARTIST

LAURA **VILLARI** – COLORIST
SIMON **BOWLAND** – LETTERER
KIRK & BAUMANN – COVER
ANTHONY **DIAL** – PRODUCTION

NATHAN **COSBY** – ASSISTANT EDITOR
MARK **PANICCIA** – EDITOR
JOE **QUESADA** – EDITOR IN CHIEF
DAN **BUCKLEY** – PUBLISHER

GATHER 'ROUND YOUNGLINGS, ALL YOU PUPS AND YOU CHICKS, ALL YOU CUBS AND YOU FOALS.

LET YOUR TALE-WEAVER SPIN YOU A SAGA YOU'VE HEARD A HUNDRED TIMES OR MORE...

...YET NO NEW BOY OR GIRL WITH A HEART OR A SOUL TIRES OF THE TELLING...

...FOR IT TELLS OF COURAGE, AND HONOR, AND ALL THOSE THINGS WE HOLD DEAR...

...EMBODIED IN TWO MIGHTY WARRIORS...

...THE CUNNING AND BRAVE LADY SHADRA, AND HER LOYAL SQUIRE GULO, FIERCEST OF THE WEASEL FOLK!

- WUNDAGORE -

...AND USED ALL HIS ARTS TO TAKE THE BEST PARTS OF ANIMALS AND HUMANS TO BREATHE LIFE INTO WE NEW MEN!

AND LO, THE HIGH EVOLUTIONARY RETREATED TO HIS HIDDEN SANCTUM DEEP WITHIN YONDER MOUNT WUNDAGORE...

FROM A WOLF THE HIGH EVOLUTIONARY CREATED THE MOST ADVANCED NEW MAN TO DATE, POSSESSED OF VAST STRENGTH AND PSYCHIC ABILITY.

...BY WIPING OUT ALL LIFE ON EARTH! HE CREATED HIS OWN LEGION OF EVIL TO DESTROY WHAT OUR FATHER HAD BUILT—ALL SEEMED LOST--

THIS CREATURE DUBBED HIMSELF THE MAN-BEAST, DESIROUS AS HE WAS TO PROVE HIS SUPERIORITY TO ALL OTHER PREDATORS THAT HAD COME BEFORE HIM...

...IF HE AND THE KNIGHTS SOUGHT THEIR DESTINY IN THE STARS AS WELL, LEAVING ONLY WE FEW BEHIND.

OUR FATHER THEN EXILED THE MAN-BEAST INTO SPACE, AND DECIDED IT WOULD BE SAFER FOR HUMAN AND NEW MAN ALIKE...

AND SHOULD YOU LOOK UP INTO THE SKY FOR THEIR RETURN, YOUNGLINGS, WISH ON THE BRIGHTEST TWINKLING POINT IN THE HEAVENS...

...AND, ONE DAY, THE ROAR OF THEIR ROCKETS SHALL FILL YOUR EARS!

SSSSSSSHHBOOM

IS THAT *THEM?* IS THAT SHADRA AND GULO?

DON'T *FOOL* US, PROSIMIA--DID YOU *MAKE* THAT HAPPEN? IS THAT PART OF YOUR *STORY?*

PERHAPS IF SOME OF YOU HAVE BEEN *NAUGHTY* AND DISOBEYED *BOVA,* SHADRA AND GULO HAVE COME TO TEACH YOU A *LESSON*--

ENOUGH OF YOUR *TALE-WEAVING,* PROSIMIA!

HELP ME HIDE THE CHILDREN IN THE *BUNKERS!*

JJJVOOOMMMMMP

THAT *DOES* IT.

THAT IS ABSOLUTELY THE *LAST* TIME I LET YOU *LAND*, KITTY.

AW, *C'MON!*

WE MADE IT IN *ONE PIECE*, RIGHT?

TELL THAT TO MY *LUNCH.*

WILL YOU GET A LOAD OF THIS, LOGAN?

USUALLY THE LOCALS WAIT AT LEAST *FIFTEEN MINUTES* BEFORE BREAKING OUT THE *TORCHES AND PITCHFORKS.*

THAT'S GOTTA BE A *LAND SPEED RECORD* FOR *MOB FORMATION!*

SPRECHEN SIE DEUTSCHE?

J-JAWOHL!

⟨WE'RE JUST PASSING *THROUGH*, BUB. WE DON'T WANT ANY *TROUBLE*--⟩

⟨THEN GO *NO FURTHER*, IF YOU VALUE YOUR SOULS!⟩

⟨THAT *WATERFALL* MARKS THE *BORDER* OF THE CURSED *RUSSOFF ESTATE!* NO GOD-FEARING MAN CAN VENTURE ANY CLOSER TO HAUNTED MOUNT *WUNDAGORE*--⟩

⟨--WITHOUT THE RISK OF *NEVER* BEING SEEN *AGAIN!*⟩

‹THANKS FOR THE **HEADS-UP**, PAL, BUT WE GOT **ORDERS**. DON'T LET THE GOOFY GETUPS **FOOL** YOU--›

‹--ME AN' THE **GIRL** KNOW HOW TO TAKE CARE OF **OURSELVES**.›

‹GREGOR, LET'S GO BACK TO THE **VILLAGE**, GET MY BROTHER-IN-LAW, YOUR COUSIN **STEFAN**, AND COME BACK TO SEE WHAT WE CAN SCAVENGE FROM THIS JET.›

‹THESE **FOREIGNERS** WILL NEVER RETURN TO IT--AND IT'D BE A **SIN** TO LET IT GO TO **WASTE**!›

YOU TELL THE NATIVES THE **REAL** REASON WE CAME TO TRANSIA?

NAH, I DIDN'T WANT TO SPEND **ALL DAY** TRYING TO **EXPLAIN** IT...

"...THAT OUR **BOSS MAN**, PROFESSOR X, IS GETTIN' A LITTLE **NERVOUS**. IT'S BEEN SO LONG SINCE WE LAST HEARD FROM OUR BIGGEST BADDIE, **MAGNETO**...

"...SO HE WANTS US TO **FIND** MAGS BEFORE HE STRIKES **AGAIN**! CHARLEY DID HIS HOMEWORK. LOOKS LIKE MAGGIE SPENT **SOME** TIME AROUND WUNDAGORE WHEN HE WAS **YOUNGER**..."

LOOK! SEE? AT THE TOP OF THE MOUNTAIN?

COULD THAT BE CAUSED BY THE WEIRD ELECTROMAGNETIC PULSES **CEREBRO** WAS DETECTING AROUND HERE?

ONLY ONE WAY TO **FIND OUT**...

YOU'D THINK THOSE HUNTERS MIGHT'VE *MENTIONED* THERE WAS A WHOLE *TOWN* UP HERE!

SEEMS DOWNRIGHT *COZY* FOR A *"FORBIDDEN"* MOUNTAIN.

ABANDONED?

HARDLY...

SNIFF SNIFF

MY *ENHANCED SENSES* ARE PICKING UP WOOD-BURNING OVENS... FRESHLY OILED MACHINERY...

...AND...

NRRRGGGGGGGGG

...*GEEZ*, MORE *ANIMAL* SCENTS THAN BACKSTAGE AT *RINGLING BROS.!*

THEY RUNNIN' A FORBIDDEN *ZOO* ON THIS MOUNTAINTOP TOO, OR--

KITTY--

DOWN!!

SHOTWANG

MAGGIE'S *WELCOME WAGON*, HUH?

SNIKT

NRRREEEEEEEEE

WELL I'M GONNA MAKE 'EM WISH THEY BROUGHT OUR *FLAMIN' FRUIT BASK--*

--WHOOOAAA!!

IT **IS** THEM! THE PROMISE OF THE SAGAS HAS BEEN **FULFILLED!**

HUSH, PROSIMIA. **BUT...** HMMM...

THEY **ARE** DRESSED NOT **UNLIKE** THE ONE CALLED **THOR...**

A THOUSAND **APOLOGIES** FOR OUR INHOSPITABLE **GREETING,** STRANGERS.

BUT THESE ARE **DANGEROUS TIMES** ON WUNDAGORE, IN DESPERATE NEED OF **HEROES...**

...BY CHANCE CAN **YOU** BE DESCRIBED IN SUCH A WAY?

I BEEN CALLED **WORSE.**

NEW MEN HAVE BEEN DISAPPEARING AT AN **ALARMING** RATE FROM OUR TINY TOWN--

--AT THE SAME TIME THOSE STRANGE **LIGHTS** BEGAN EMANATING FROM THE PEAK **ABOVE!**

"YOU TRY CHECKING IT OUT **YOURSELF** FIRST, BESSIE?"

"BOVA, INDEED, I **DID...**

"...LAST NIGHT I MUSTERED MY COURAGE AS BEST I **COULD** AND VENTURED INTO THE MOUNTAIN AS FAR AS OUR CODES **ALLOW...** AS FAR AS ONE NOT **KNIGHTED** MAY!

"**THERE** I SAW..."

"...A *CAPED* FIGURE WHO APPEARED AS IF...HE WAS LEVITATING-- *ARRANGING*--HUGE PIECES OF OUR FATHER'S OLD *MACHINERY*...

"...SIMPLY BY *WAVING HIS HANDS!*"

BINGO. THAT'D BE OUR OLD BUDDY *"THE MASTER OF MAGNETISM,"* ALRIGHT.

KITTY. GO BACK TO THE BLACKBIRD, RADIO *CHARLEY.* TELL 'IM HE NEEDS TO SEND THE REST OF THE *X-MEN.*

I'M GONNA HAVE BESSIE-- *BOVA.* --LEAD ME TO WHERE MAGS IS HANGIN' HIS *HELMET.*

YOU SIT TIGHT WITH THE *REST* OF THE KIDS, WAIT FOR THE *CAVALRY* TO ARRIVE--

THE *REST* OF THE KIDS? WHAT'S *THAT* SUPPOSED TO MEAN?

AND WHY CAN'T I GO *WITH* YOU? YOU MIGHT NEED ME TO--

YOU KNOW, I'M OFFICIALLY *TIRED* OF YOU *QUESTIONIN'* MY ORDERS EVERY FIVE MINUTES!

NEWSFLASH, CHICKIE: THIS AIN'T A *DEMOCRACY.*

JUST *DO* IT.

[65]

THESE *TUNNELS* LEAD RIGHT FROM OUR VILLAGE TO THE *HEART* OF THE HOLLOW MOUNTAIN.

THERE'S NOT MUCH TO *SEE*--ONLY SOME OLD *EQUIPMENT* THE HIGH EVOLUTIONARY LEFT BEHIND WHEN HE WENT INTO *SPACE*--

--BUT SOME OF HIS WONDERS DO *REMAIN.*

LIKE THE *ROUND TABLE* OF THE NOBLE *KNIGHTS OF WUNDAGORE!*

HERE SAT *SQUIRE GULO*-- FIERCEST OF THE *WEASEL FOLK.*

OUR TALE-WEAVER, *PROSIMIA,* SAYS YOU *REMIND* HIM OF GULO...

...WHO WAS EVOLVED, OF COURSE, FROM A... *WOLVERINE.*

WOLVERINE THINKS HE'S SO *WISE* AND EVERYTHING JUST 'CAUSE HE'S, LIKE, A *MILLION* YEARS OLD...

WAIT...

URRRRRN

ARE THOSE... THE *HUNTERS* FROM BEFORE?

DID THEY TRY TO *BOOST* OUR PLANE?!

THE AUTOMATIC *DEFENSES* DIDN'T GET THEM *ALL*--

--*ONE* MADE OFF WITH OUR *RADIO!*

I BETTER WARN WOLVERINE *REINFORCEMENTS* ARE GONNA BE IN *SHORT SUPPLY* UNTIL WE CAN FIND ANOTHER SOURCE OF *COMMUNICATIONS!*

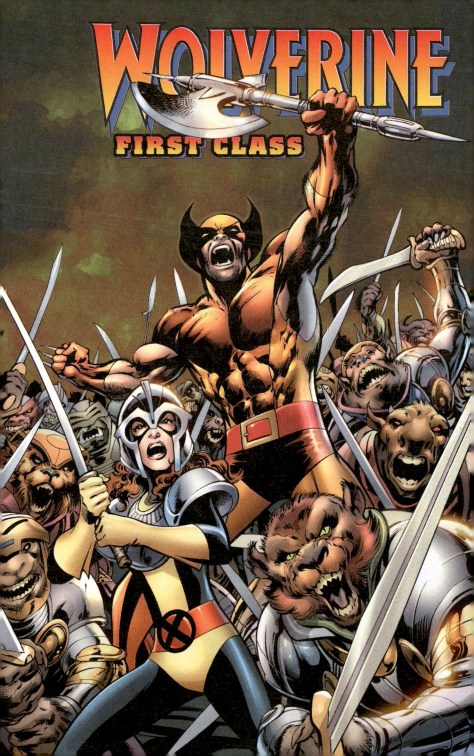

ORGH!

VRAAARR!

SCRAW!

CRAK!

MWUF!

THE FACT I COULD *SMELL* ENEMIES SNEAKING UP ON ME FROM A *MILE AWAY* DIDN'T HURT, EITHER.

BACK! *BACK,* BLAST YOU!

GRRRRR.... THERE'S *TOO MANY* OF THEM!

WE CAN'T RISK SOME *GETTING THROUGH* WHILE THE VILLAGE IS UNDEFENDED!

WE HAVE TO *FALL BACK--* TOWARD TOWN!

SHOW ME THE *QUICKEST* WAY OUT OF HERE, PROSIMIA!

Y-YES, *AT ONCE,* LADY SHAD--

I MEAN, *LADY PRYDE!*

IS THERE NOT **SOME** WAY YOU CAN BE CONTENT JUST TO **LIVE?**

CAN THERE BE NO **PEACE** FOR YOU OTHER THAN THAT OF THE BATTLEFIELD **AFTER** THE BATTLE, WITH ALL YOUR ENEMIES--

WHY, MAN-BEAST?

WHY DO YOU SEEK TO DESTROY ALL THAT **LIVES,** BEGINNING WITH YOUR FELLOW **NEW MEN?**

WHAT IS IT ABOUT THE DRIVE TO **EXIST** THAT MAKES ONE WISH TO SNUFF OUT **OTHER** EXISTENCES?

--SLAIN?

A PSIONIC **ILLUSION,** FATHER!

CREATED BY THE VAST MENTAL POWERS **YOU** GAVE ME!

AAARRRGGHH!

SO...**THIS** WAS YOUR SCHEME?

YOUR TITANIC **NARCISSISM** DISGUSTS ME AS ALWAYS, FATHER!

DESTROYING YOU IS MERELY A HAPPY **SIDE** BENEFIT...

TO CAUSE... SUCH A **TUMULT...** WITHIN MY BELOVED **WUNDAGORE...**TO LURE ME **BACK** FROM THE **DISTANT STARS...**

...AND **SLAY** ME?

...OF REMOVING THAT **ARMOR** YOU WEAR, WHICH WILL AMPLIFY MY **OWN** POWER...

...TO THAT OF A **GOD!**

GASP! AT LAST! I'M SAFE!

WAIT...WHAT DID I JUST DO?

FOR THE FIRST TIME IN MY LIFE I WAS FACED WITH FIGHT-OR-FLIGHT...

...AND CHOSE DOOR NUMBER TWO! LEAVIN' KITTY AND BESSIE IN THE LURCH!

WHAT'S WRONG WITH ME?

"GOTTA BE... CHROME-DOME WASN'T KIDDING WHEN HE SAID HE REMOVED THE BESTIAL PART OF ME!

"HE WIPED AWAY NOT JUST MY BERSERKER RAGES--BUT THE PREDATORY INSTINCTS THAT WENT WITH 'EM!"

I'M--I'M NORMAL! STILL A MUTANT, SURE, BUT NO GOOD IN A SCRAP ANYMORE! AN'... AN'...

...MAYBE THAT'S THE BEST THING ANYONE'S EVER DONE FOR ME!

I CAN FINALLY STOP RAGIN'! STOP FIGHTIN'! STOP BEIN' A PAWN FOR ANYONE WHO WANTS SOMETHIN' DIRTY DONE!

THE ARMY... THE SPOOKS... AND YEAH, EVEN CHARLEY.

I COULD JUST WALK DOWN THAT HILL... DISAPPEAR...

...AND FIND SOME PEACE.

NO! THIS ONE'S *FINAL CHAPTER* IS NOT YET *WRIT--*

STAY *BACK,* YOU FOOL!

AAGHGHGHH...!!!

FOR... AS LONG AS... YOUR *TALE* GOES ON... LADY PRYDE--

THE DREAM CAN... *NEVER DIE...*

PROSIMIA...!

GRRRRRR RRRR....

PROSIMIA...

SNIKT!

SNIKT!

YOU GONNA SEND SOME OF THAT SUPER-SCIENCE MOJO *MY* WAY, TOO?

I DON'T SEE *WHY*...

...SINCE I DID NOT ALTER *YOUR* GENETIC MAKEUP IN THE *FIRST PLACE*.

WHAAAAAT? THEN WHAT WAS THAT *LIGHT SHOW* BACK THERE?

THE *FLAW* I SAW IN YOUR CHARACTER, SIR WOLVERINE, WAS THE *MISERY* YOU PUT YOURSELF THROUGH FOR BEING WHAT YOU *ARE*.

THE *ONLY* INSTINCTS I SEE IN YOU, "LOGAN"... ARE *KNIGHTLY* ONES.

EVEN WHEN YOU THOUGHT YOU HAD *LOST* YOUR BERSERKER NATURE, YOU RETURNED *HERE*, TO *BATTLE*, TO HELP YOUR FRIENDS.

REMEMBER THAT.

AND HEY, LOOKS LIKE *I* HAVE THE *"EYE OF THE TIGER,"* HUH, TEACH?

YEAH, OKAY. I'LL TRY TO GIVE YOU *MORE* RESPONSIBILITY ON THE *NEXT* MISSION, I *PROMISE*.

DOES THAT MEAN I GET TO FLY THE *BLACKBIRD* ON THE WAY HOME?

OH, NO. NO, NO, NO. NO WAY.

BUT YOU *PROMISED*!

I MADE A *PROMISE*, NOT A *DEATH WISH*!

AND SO THE LAST KNIGHTS OF WUNDAGORE FLEW AWAY ON THEIR *BLACK BIRD*...

...BUT THE *MODEL* OF THEIR HEROISM SHALL STAY BEHIND *FOREVER.* THE END.

WELL *DONE,* DICERO!

I CAN TELL *PROSIMIA* LIKED YOUR TALE VERY MUCH, TOO.

DON'T FORGET TO GIVE HIM *HIS* COPY!

OKAY!

WHO WOULD LIKE TO WEAVE *THEIR* TALE, NEXT?

ME! ME! I WILL!

HERE YOU GO, PROSIMIA.

End

"...IF WE'RE NOT *TOO LATE* ALREADY..."

HEY, WHEN WE JOIN ALPHA FLIGHT...

...WILL I GET A *BETTER* COSTUME?

'CAUSE I GOT TO TELL YOU, THIS GENERIC *X-HOODIE* IS REALLY *STIFLING* MY *INDIVIDUALITY*...

WASN'T SO *LONG* AGO THE ONLY THING I COULD EXPECT FROM *ALPHA* WAS A PUNCH IN THE *MOUTH*.

OH, WOW. SO YOU MANAGED TO TOTALLY *TICK OFF* THE *OTHER* HERO TEAM YOU WERE A MEMBER OF TOO?

WHAT A SHOCK.

HA, HA. IT'S A LITTLE *DIFFERENT* IN THIS CASE, KID. *CHARLEY'LL* BE *MIFFED* FOR A WHILE OVER THIS, BUT ONE DAY HE'LL GET OVER IT. I'M JUST *ONE* OF A *DOZEN* X-MEN.

WITH *ALPHA FLIGHT*, THOUGH, I WASN'T JUST THE *TOP DOG*...

...I WAS *FIRST* O' THE *LITTER*.

JIMMY HUDSON, HEAD OF CANADA'S SUPERHUMAN PROGRAM, *DEPARTMENT H*, FOUND ME WHILE HE AND HIS WIFE WERE *HIKIN'* ON THEIR *HONEYMOON*.

NOTHING LIKE FINDIN' A STARK RAVIN' *WILD MAN* WITH NO MEMORY AT ALL -- NOT EVEN O' HOW HIS BONES GOT LACED WITH UNBREAKABLE *ADAMANTIUM* -- TO RUIN A *ROMANTIC EVENING*, HUH?

DEPARTMENT H TOOK ME IN, *TAMED* ME, *TRAINED* ME, GAVE ME A *PURPOSE:*

DEFENDIN' THE COUNTRY FROM *MONSTERS* LIKE WENDIGO--AND THE *HULK*.

TAKES ONE TO *BEAT* ONE, RIGHT?

THE *BIG BRASS* THOUGHT 'CAUSE O' MY *EXPERIENCE,* I SHOULD LEAD THE WHOLE *TEAM* OF SUPER-CANUCKS THEY WERE TRYIN' TO FORM...

...AND, DUMB AS I *WAS* BACK THEN, I THOUGHT THAT MIGHT ACTUALLY BE A *GOOD IDEA...*

WE GOT A *BONAFIDE RED BALL* ON OUR HANDS, LOGAN.

HOSTAGE SITUATION AT LA CITADELLE IN QUEBEC CITY--EARLY REPORTS SUGGEST AT LEAST *SOME* OF THE PERPS ARE *SUPERHUMANS.*

NOW I KNOW YOU LIKE TO WORK *SOLO,* BUT THE MINISTRY OF *DEFENSE* IS INSISTING YOU BRING A *STRIKE TEAM* ON THIS ONE--

RESIGNED

H.I.A.

FOR ONCE I *AGREE* WITH 'EM. A *HOSTILE EXTRACTION* WITH MULTIPLE TARGETS NEEDS PLENTY O' *WARM BODIES.*

LESSEE HERE... I'LL TAKE...

SOUNDS LIKE MY KINDA *SCRAP.*

[101]

CODENAME: **SNOWBIRD**
POWERS: SHAPESHIFTING, FLIGHT, STRENGTH

...SNOWBIRD. OTHER THAN *ME*, SHE'S GOT THE MOST *OPERATIONAL EXPERIENCE*...

CODENAME: **AURORA**
POWERS: SPEED, FLIGHT

...AND *AURORA*. SHE'S A LITTLE *FLIGHTY* FOR MY TASTES, BUT SHE'S OUR *SPEEDSTER*, AND WE'LL NEED TO HIT THESE JOKERS *FAST*.

AND... UM...

CODENAME: **SHAMAN**
POWERS: 1ST NATIONS MAGIC

...GIMME THE *DOC*. WHAT'D THEY END UP CALLING HIM? *"SHAMAN?"*

YOU *SURE*? MICHAEL HAS NEVER BEEN IN THE *FIELD* BEFORE--HE'S ALWAYS JUST BEEN OUR MYSTICAL *ADVISOR*--

THAT SO? WELL, WHEN *INNOCENT LIVES* ARE AT STAKE, JIMMY...

...NEVER *HURTS* TO HAVE A LITTLE *MAGIC* ON YOUR SIDE.

ALL RIGHT, GANG! *SADDLE UP!* I'LL GIVE YOU THE *SITREP* EN ROUTE.

I'M SO *GRATEFUL* YOU SELECTED ME FOR THIS TEAM, M'SIEUR LOGAN.

IF YOU HAVE SOME FREE TIME *AFTERWARD*, I'D LIKE TO SHOW YOU *HOW* MUCH...

ER... *THANKS*, JEANNE-MARIE...

IT WOULD BE BEST FOR ALL IF YOU SIMPLY KEPT YOUR MIND ON THE MISSION, AURORA.

OH, *PARDONNEZ-MOI*, ICE QUEEN...

SNOWBIRD.

MAIS NATURELLEMENT...

[104]

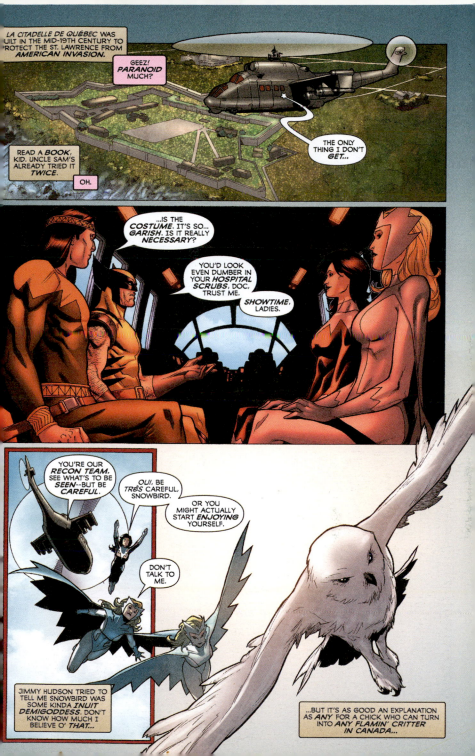

...AND USE WHAT SHE CALLS *"POSTCOGNITIVE SIGHT"*...

...TO SEE A VISION OF *ANY EVENT* UP TO *SIX HOURS OLD.*

WHOEVER THESE HOSTILES *ARE,* THEY'RE DEFINITELY NOT *AMATEURS.*

THE MINUTE THEY SECURED *LA CITADELLE,* THEY HUNKERED DOWN BEHIND HER FORTIFICATIONS.

MY MEN HAVE NO IDEA *WHERE* THEY ARE INSIDE THE FORTRESS--OR EVEN *HOW MANY* THERE ARE!

I COUNTED **FOURTEEN**.

YAAH!!

IT TOOK ME ABOUT **TWO-AND-A-HALF MINUTES** TO CASE THE ENTIRE FORTRESS.

AND YOU KNOW, IN THAT ENTIRE TIME, I DIDN'T SEE SNOWBIRD ANYWHERE... *TSK, TSK.* DERELICTION OF DUTY. *PAS BON...*

DE TOUTE FAÇON, THEY'VE HERDED THE GARRISON, ALL THE TOURISTS AND STAFF INTO THE MUSEUM...

...ALONG WITH A **GOAT,** FOR SOME REASON...

THAT'D BE **"BAPTISTE,"** THE REGIMENTAL MASCOT, WEAPON X.

YOU KNOW MY **CIPHER-CODE.** THAT PEGS YOU AS **INT BRANCH*,** BUB.

WHAT'RE **YOU** DOING HERE? THOUGHT THIS WAS STRICTLY A LOCAL **LAW ENFORCE-MENT** DEAL--

KINNEY, 2 INT PLATOON, **OTTAWA.** THIS IS A MATTER OF **NATIONAL SECURITY** NOW, STRAIGHT FROM THE **MINISTRY.**

THE **GOVERNOR GENERAL** IS A PRISONER IN THERE.

WHAAAAAT? *SHE IS?* WHEN WERE YOU PLANNIN' ON TELLIN' MY **DEPARTMENT H** CREW THAT--

*: "INT(ELLIGENCE) BRANCH," CANADIAN MILITARY INTELLIGENCE.

WHENEVER I BLOODY WELL *FELT* LIKE IT. WE'RE JUST LUCKY WE'VE KEPT THE *MEDIA'S* NOSES OUT OF IT.

YOU MAY STILL BE *RINGMASTER* OF THIS TRAVELING FREAKSHOW, BUT NOW IT'S *INT BRANCH'S* CIRCUS.

YOU WEIRDOS' *A-NUMBER-ONE PRIORITY* IS TO FIND *WHERE* THEY'RE KEEPING THE *GOVERNOR GENERAL.*

THEY TOOK HER TO THE *CELLAR* IN HER *RESIDENCE* ON THE GROUNDS.

WHA-- EEEEEKK!!

AND WOLVERINE... WE SHOULD PROCEED WITH CAUTION.

"ONE OF THE TERRORISTS IS DEFINITELY A SUPERHUMAN."

THERE'S A *REASON* THEY CALLED *US* IN AND NOT THE *MOUNTIES,* DARLIN'.

OKAY WITH *YOU* TO CUT TO THE HEROICS, INT MAN?

I *SUPPOSE...* BUT YOU GIVE ME *CONSTANT* REPORTS OF YOUR PROGRESS, WEAPON X, OR I'LL--

YEAH, YEAH. SEND ME TO BED WITH *NO SUPPER.*

SYNCHRONIZE YOUR *WATCHES,* PEOPLE. I'LL EXTRACT THE GOVERNOR GENERAL--

SHE'S THE OFFICIAL GOVERNMENT REPRESENTATIVE OF THE QUEEN OF CANADA--

WHOA! THERE'S A *QUEEN* OF CANADA?

ER...SORT OF. THE QUEEN OF *CANADA* IS WHOEVER HAPPENS TO BE QUEEN OF *ENGLAND*--

HUH? YOU GUYS ARE PART OF *ENGLAND*?

NO. WELL, WE *USED* TO BE. BUT NOW WE'RE *NOT*--

THEN WHY CAN THE ENGLISH QUEEN PUSH YOU AROUND?

SHE *CAN'T*!

I MEAN...SHE *CAN*, SINCE THE GOVERNOR GENERAL CAN *VETO*, AS HER REP, *ANY* GOVERNMENT DECISION...

AND YOU'RE TRYING TO *SAVE* THIS PERSON?

JUST SHUT UP AND *LISTEN*, YANK:

GOUVERNEUR GENERAL

IT'S *TIME*.

BUT BE *CAREFUL*. THE ENCHANTMENT WILL BE *BROKEN* IF WE MAKE ANY SUDDEN...

KRASSSHH!

RROOOAAR!

...MOVEMENTS.

DUST FROM THE REALM OF *DREAMS* WILL PUT BOTH ENEMY *AND* INNOCENT TO SLEEP--

--BUT PERHAPS THEN, WE WILL HAVE A *CLEARER* VIEW OF--

UNNH!!

MICHAEL! NON!

KRAK!

I AM NOT ALL THAT TERRIBLY *STRONG*--

--BUT WHEN ONE CAN LAND *FIFTY PUNCHES A SECOND*, YOU DO NOT *NEED* TO BE!

BUDDA! BUDDA! BUDDA! BUDDA!

SHAMAN! *REMERCIEZ DIEU!* THE KEVLAR LINING OF YOUR OUTFIT SAVED YOU, *OUI?*

I CHANGED MY MIND.

I LIKE THE COSTUME.

MICHAEL--*LOOK*-- THE MAN WHOSE *MASK* AURORA DESTROYED--

SACRE BLEU!

THIS... THIS *IS* A DEVELOPMENT...

"...IS THERE ANY WAY TO *WARN* WOLVERINE?"

WE *PROS* CALL IT "*ADRENAL DUMP*"--THE BODY'S VERY OWN *TURBO-BOOST* INJECTION.

...OR *END* 'EM.

EVEN OLD HANDS LIKE *ME* CAN GET SO *AMPED* UP EXECUTIN' AN OP WE GET *SLOPPY*--MISS THE LITTLE THINGS THAT CAN *SAVE* LIVES...

LIKE AN *ODOR* I DIDN'T REALIZE MY ENHANCED SENSES WERE TELLIN' ME WAS ALL *OVER* THESE BADDIES...

...*ESPECIALLY* THE ONE SNEAKIN' UP *BEHIND* ME.

A SCENT ALMOST *UNDETECTABLE* TO ME...

SKRASH!

...'CAUSE IT WAS SO CLOSE TO MY *OWN*.

SWAMMM!

WOLVERINE-- QUICKLY!

WHILE I HAVE HIM OFF-BALANCE--

BLAST IT, CITADEL, YOU GOTTA LISTEN TO ME--YOU'RE RIGHT. THE PUBLIC NEEDS TO HEAR YOUR STORY- AND SO DO I!

WHERE WAS THIS CLINIC YOU WERE TAKEN TO? WHO OPERATED ON YOU? COULD YOU RECOGNIZE ANY OF 'EM IF YOU SAW THEM AGAIN?

I AIN'T TELLING YOU JACK EXCEPT MY NAME, RANK AND SERIAL NUMBER-

YEAH YEAH! THAT'S A START!

WHAT'S YOUR REAL NAME, SOLDIER? WHAT UNIT WERE YOU ASSI--

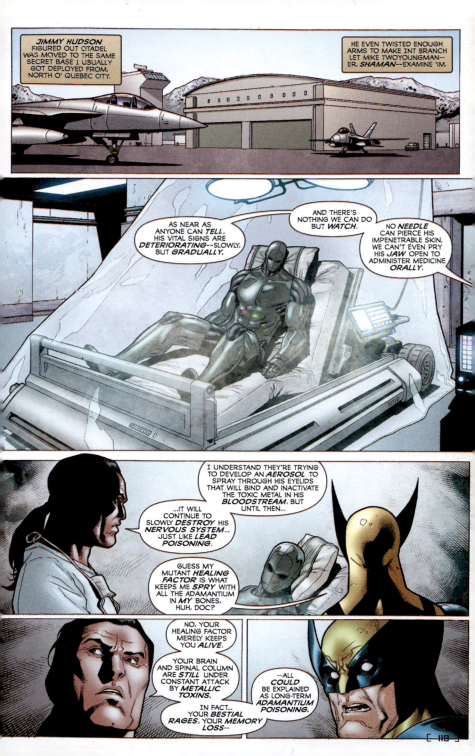

JIMMY HUDSON FIGURED OUT CITADEL WAS MOVED TO THE SAME SECRET BASE I USUALLY GOT DEPLOYED FROM, NORTH O' QUEBEC CITY.

HE EVEN TWISTED ENOUGH ARMS TO MAKE INT BRANCH LET MIKE TWOYOUNGMAN-- ER, *SHAMAN*--EXAMINE 'IM.

AS NEAR AS ANYONE CAN *TELL*, HIS VITAL SIGNS ARE *DETERIORATING*--SLOWLY, BUT *GRADUALLY*.

AND THERE'S NOTHING WE CAN DO BUT *WATCH*.

NO *NEEDLE* CAN PIERCE HIS IMPENETRABLE SKIN. WE CAN'T EVEN PRY HIS *JAW* OPEN TO ADMINISTER MEDICINE *ORALLY*.

I UNDERSTAND THEY'RE TRYING TO DEVELOP AN *AEROSOL* TO SPRAY THROUGH HIS EYELIDS THAT WILL BIND AND INACTIVATE THE TOXIC METAL IN HIS *BLOODSTREAM*, BUT UNTIL THEN...

...IT WILL CONTINUE TO SLOWLY *DESTROY* HIS *NERVOUS SYSTEM*... JUST LIKE *LEAD POISONING*.

GUESS MY MUTANT *HEALING FACTOR* IS WHAT KEEPS ME *SPRY* WITH ALL THE ADAMANTIUM IN *MY* BONES, HUH, DOC?

NO, YOUR HEALING FACTOR MERELY KEEPS YOU *ALIVE*.

YOUR BRAIN AND SPINAL COLUMN ARE *STILL* UNDER CONSTANT ATTACK BY *METALLIC TOXINS*.

IN FACT... YOUR *BESTIAL RAGES*, YOUR *MEMORY LOSS*--

--ALL *COULD* BE EXPLAINED AS LONG-TERM *ADAMANTIUM POISONING*.

I FELT LIKE I'D JUST BEEN PUSHED OFF A CLIFF.

THE SAME UNBREAKABLE CLAWS AND SKELETON THAT HAD SAVED MY HIDE MORE TIMES THAN I CARED TO REMEMBER--

--WERE ACTUALLY TRYING TO KILL ME.

AND THE GOVERNMENT I TRUSTED, THAT HAD GIVEN ME A REASON TO LIVE, COULD BE BEHIND IT...

...OR WAS REFUSING TO TELL ME WHO WAS, WHICH MAYBE WAS JUST AS BAD.

PLAYING THE GOOD SOLDIER WAS STARTIN' TO LOOK NOT SO GOOD ANYMORE.

CITADEL AND HIS GUYS TOOK ORDERS AND KEPT THEIR YAPS SHUT--AND LOOK HOW THEY TURNED OUT.

IT SO HAPPENED THAT KINNEY HAD ARRANGED A MEETING WITH US AND SOME AMERICAN BRAINIAC THAT DAY WHO MIGHT ADVISE DEPARTMENT H ON THE RECRUITMENT OF MUTANTS.

GOOD OL' CHARLEY.

THAT'S WHEN HE MADE THE PITCH FOR ME TO JOIN THE X-MEN.

SOMEHOW HE KNEW I'D BE IN THE MOOD TO LISTEN.

'COURSE COLONEL KINNEY WASN'T TOO THRILLED TO HEAR I WAS REJOINING THE PRIVATE SECTOR.

TOO FLAMIN' BAD.

BUT...

...WE WERE STILL *TOO LATE.*

HE *NEVER* REGAINED CONSCIOUSNESS.

I'M SORRY, LOGAN.

GEEZ...LOOKS LIKE HE LOST HIS *BEST* FRIEND.

I THINK IT'S *WORSE* THAN THAT.

HE LOST A LINK TO HIS *PAST.*

AND A GUY LIKE *WOLVERINE...*

... DOESN'T KNOW HOW MANY OF *THOSE* HE HAS *LEFT...*

CITADEL

FRED VAN LENTE - WRITER

CHRIS SOTOMAYOR - COLORIST

ESPIN & GURU eFX - COVER

JOE SABINO - PRODUCTION

JOE QUESADA - EDITOR IN CHIEF

CLAYTON HENRY - ARTIST

SIMON BOWLAND - LETTERER

NATHAN COSBY - ASST. EDITOR

MARK PANICCIA - EDITOR

DAN BUCKLEY - PUBLISHER

REMOTES, BEVERAGE, TRAIL MIX, TEAM YEARBOOK WITH STATS...

ALL WITHIN FOREARM'S LENGTH FROM MY CHAIR, SO I WON'T HAVE TO EVEN LEAN OVER TO PICK 'EM UP...

PERFECT.

SURE YOU WON'T CHANGE YOUR MIND AND JOIN US, LOGAN?

THIS IS THE LAST NIGHT DR. MacTAGGERT AND YOUR OLD TEAMMATE BANSHEE WILL BE VISITING.

TOMORROW MORNING THEY RETURN TO DR. MacTAGGART'S MUTANT RESEARCH FACILITY ON *MUIR ISLAND*, IN SCOTLAND.

NAH, YOU GUYS ENJOY YOUR DINNER AND A SHOW.

TONIGHT IS THE SEVENTH GAME OF THE *STANLEY CUP* FINALS, AND I AIN'T MISSING IT FOR A SINGLE FLAMIN' THING!

YOU WILL STILL KEEP ONE EYE ON MY BABY SISTER, WON'T YOU, LOGAN?

⟨NOW YOU *BEHAVE* YOURSELF, ILLYANA NIKOLIEVNA, AND DO *WHATEVER* MR. WOLVERINE SAYS.⟩ *

⟨I PROMISE, PIOTR NIKOLAIEVITCH.⟩

*: TRANSLATED FROM RUSSIAN, COLOSSUS AND ILLYANA'S NATIVE TONGUE.--MOSCOW MARK

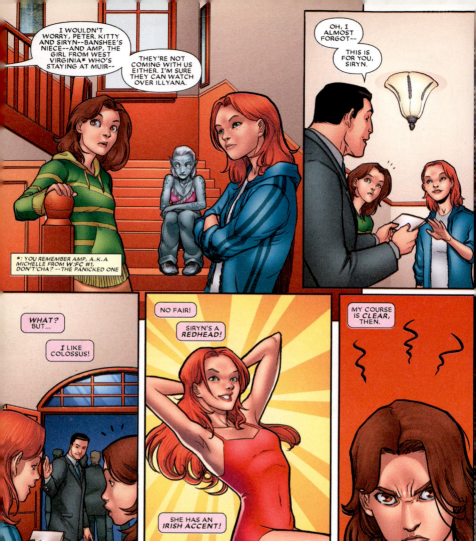

I WOULDN'T WORRY, PETER. KITTY AND SIRYN--BANSHEE'S NIECE--AND AMP, THE GIRL FROM WEST VIRGINIA* WHO'S STAYING AT MUIR--

THEY'RE NOT COMING WITH US EITHER. I'M SURE THEY CAN WATCH OVER ILLYANA.

*: YOU REMEMBER AMP, A.K.A. MICHELLE FROM W:FC #1, DON'T'CHA? --THE PANICKED ONE

OH, I ALMOST FORGOT--

THIS IS FOR YOU, SIRYN.

WHAT? BUT...

I LIKE COLOSSUS!

NO FAIR!

SIRYN'S A REDHEAD!

SHE HAS AN IRISH ACCENT!

SHE'S CLOSER TO COLOSSUS IN AGE!

SHE'S ...SHE'S WAY PRETTIER THAN ME!

MY COURSE IS CLEAR, THEN.

I MUST DESTROY HER.

ALRIGHT, LISTEN UP:

YOU LADIES CAN DO WHATEVER YOU *WANT* TONIGHT, I COULD CARE LESS...

...SO LONG AS YOU *DON'T* INTERRUPT MY *GAME.* I MISS ONE *SECOND* O' *REGULATION* TIME...

...AND I TURN THE *LOT* O' YOU INTO *GIRL-KABOBS.*

SNIKT!

GOT ME?

MR. LOGAN IS SO *FUNNY.*

OH, NO, NO, NO.

HE'S *SERIOUS.*

SO...WHAT DO YOU WANT TO DO?

DUNNO. WHAT DO *YOU* WANT TO DO?

DUNNO...

D'YE KNOW WHAT COULD BE FUN?

I'D LOVE TO TAKE A LOOK AT THIS *DANGER ROOM* I'VE HEARD SO MUCH ABOUT. IT'S IN THE BASEMENT, RIGHT?

OH... I DON'T KNOW...

I'M NOT REALLY ALLOWED TO RUN IT BY *MYSELF...*

AW, C'MON, KITTY! *PLEEEEEASE?* JUST A PEEK! WHO'S TO *KNOW?*

WELL...

IF I *DON'T*, I *KNOW* WHAT'S GONNA HAPPEN...

HA HA HA! THAT'S *RIGHT*, DARLING! THE SCARED LITTLE GIRL WOULDN'T EVEN LET ME LOOK *INSIDE* THE DANGER ROOM! SHE WAS PROBABLY AFRAID OF HAVING HER *TOYS* TAKEN AWAY!

HO, HO, HO! I'M GLAD I CHOSE A REAL, SOPHISTICATED WOMAN, LIKE *YOU* OVER *THAT* GOODY-TWO-SHOES!

THE ELEVATOR TO THE LOWER LEVELS IS *THIS* WAY!

BRILLIANT!

THIS PLACE IS REALLY SOMETHING *ELSE*...

IT'S BUILT LIKE A FORTRESS! I BET *NOBODY* CAN GET IN HERE!

YOU'D *THINK*, AMP, BUT IT ACTUALLY GETS INVADED AND TRASHED QUITE A LOT.

LIKE...ONCE A *MONTH*, IT SEEMS LIKE...

PROFESSOR X CHANGES THE ACCESS CODES EVERY DAY, SO I'LL HAVE TO OPEN UP FROM THE *INSIDE*.

SWOOOSH!

VOILA!

WOW! KITTY, YOU'RE AMAZING!

WHAT MY COUSIN *BLACK TOM* AND I WOULDN'T HAVE GIVEN FOR SOMEONE LIKE *YE* WHEN WE WERE COMMITTIN' *ROBBERIES* TOGETHER!

YE'RE LIKE A NATURAL BORN CRIMINAL!

I AM? GEE...

I DON'T SEE WHAT'S SO *"DANGER-Y"* ABOUT IT.

IT'S *NOT*-- NOT WITHOUT A *TRAINING PROGRAM* RUNNING.

...THAT'S ONE OF THE NICEST THINGS ANYONE'S EVER SAID TO ME...

OH, SO YE'RE HOLDIN' *OUT* ON ME, THEN?

I AM *NOT!*

YE SAID YE'D LET ME *SEE* THE DANGER ROOM, RIGHT? AND I'M NOT REALLY *SEEIN'* IT WITHOUT A *PROGRAM* RUNNIN', NOW *AM I?*

ER...

YE *SAID I COULD!*

WELL... WHEN YOU PUT IT *THAT* WAY...

BEEBOOBOO

JUST TO BE *SAFE*, THOUGH, I'M ONLY RUNNING THE *EARLIEST* PROGRAM I CAN FIND...

SHWWSSHHH!

SHWWSSHHH!

[131]

EEK!

BZWAAPP!

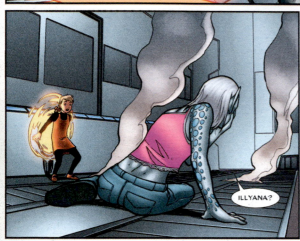

ILLYANA?

WHERE ARE YOU?

OOOF!

?

KLUNK

PROGRAM PAUSE

0:60

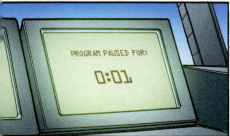

SCANNING FOR ENEMIES...

SCANNING...

KLANK! KLANK! KLANK! KLANK! KLANK!

SCANNING...

KLANK! KLANK! KLANK! KLANK! KLANK!

SCANNING...

DING!

SCANNING FOR ENEMIES...

S W I S H

SCANNING...

HAMMERSKJOLD HELPS TEE UP SERGEI KOSOLOV...

KOSOLOV PLAYS THE BOARDS...

KLANK!

KLANK!

KLANK!

KLANK!

SCANNING...

ENEMY LOCATED

KOSOLOV CHALLENGED BY TYLER...

KLANK!

KLANK! KLANK!

ENEMY LOCATED

KOSOLOV THREW OFF THE GLOVES WITH TYLER IN A SPIRITED BOUT IN GAME FOUR...

KLANK!

KLANK! KLANK!

ENEMY LOCATED

ENEMY LOCATED

ENEMY LOCATED

NO SCORE JUST PAST THE THREE MARK IN PERIOD TWO...

KLANK!

KLANK! KLANK!

HERE'S IWANIEC, WORKING HIS WAY THROUGH MACMILLER, CONNECTING WITH SAREVA, AND SAREVA WILL SEND HIM PACKING...

TELLER GETS HIS MARCHING ORDERS FROM KOSOLOV--THEN GETS CREAMED IN THE CORNER BY TYLER!! OH, THAT WAS BRUTAL!

HOW ABOUT TYLER, ALL EIGHT OF HIS GOALS IN THE PLAYOFFS COMING ON THE ROAD...

HAMMERSKJOLD AVOIDS THE BRUNT OF THAT HIT FROM DRUETT...

CALGARY BACK HOME ON HOME ICE--

SAREVA TO TYLER!

TO PETERSON!

KOSOLOV!

MCDOUGAL!

ROMOLA!

TO PETERSON AGAIN!!!

SHRAAKK!!

BOOOOMMM!!

--WATCH HOCKEY!

WHEN I FEEL LIKE IT!

FOR AS LONG AS I FEEL LIKE IT!

IT'S MY MORAL RIGHT AS A CANADIAN.

DOWN TO THE FRONT--

KOSOLOV DROPS IT--

IWANIEC FIRES--

KRSSSH

N...NO...

NO...
HOCKEY...
NO...

GRRRAAAAAAAAAa...

'ROUND MIDNIGHT:

DID YOU *SEE* THAT, LOGAN? IT WAS THE MOST AMAZING ENDING TO ANY PLAYOFF GAME *EVER!*

WE CAUGHT THE END AT THE RESTAURANT.

NO SCORE UNTIL OVERTIME--

AND THE WINNING GOAL SCORES ON A *FACE-OFF!*

SO *YOU'VE* GOT BE HAPPY, EH, MEIN HERR? WANT TO BREAK OUT THE--

⌐SIGH⌐

THE NEXT MORNING:

AGAIN-- I COULDN'T BE SORRIER, AMP.

EH. DON'T WORRY ABOUT IT. WATER UNDER THE BRIDGE.

NO, SERIOUSLY-- I'M *TRYIN'* TO BE GOOD. I AM.

IT'S JUST... I WAS SO BAD FOR SO LONG, I'M OUT OF *PRACTICE!*

BOTTOM LINE IS--NO STUPID LITTLE *BOY* SHOULD STAND IN THE WAY O' OUR FRIENDSHIP!

SISTERHOOD!

ALRIGHT...

...BUT I'VE ALREADY FORGOTTEN ABOUT DMITRI, ANYWAY. CONSIDER HIM *YOURS.*

I'VE MOVED ON TO BIGGER AND BETTER PROSPECTS...

"Little Girls"

FRED VAN LENTE — WRITER

SALVA ESPIN — ARTIST

CHRIS SOTOMAYOR — COLORIST

VC'S RUS WOOTON — LETTERER

ESPIN & GURU — COVER

PAUL ACERIOS — PRODUCTION

NATHAN COSBY — ASSISTANT EDITOR

MARK PANICCIA — EDITOR

JOE QUESADA — EDITOR IN CHIEF

DAN BUCKLEY — PUBLISHER

LISTEN *UP*, KIDS.

IT'S TIME FOR ANOTHER THRILLING INSTALLMENT O' "WOLVERINE'S FACTS YOU CAN *USE*."

LET'S SAY YOU NEED TO CLANDESTINELY PENETRATE A HIGH-SECURITY PERIMETER PATROLLED SHOULDER-TO-SHOULDER BY MOOKS IN *INFRARED GOGGLES*...

(C'MON, THAT'S HAPPENED TO MOST O' YOU AT LEAST ONCE OR *TWICE* IN YOUR LIVES, RIGHT?)

...WELL, YOU KNOW WHAT'S TOTALLY *INVISIBLE* TO THERMAL VISION, DON'T YOU?

THAT'S RIGHT.

REINDEER HIDE.

THE THICK FUR, SKIN AND BLUBBER WON'T LET ANY O' YOUR *HEAT SIGNATURE* SEEP THROUGH.

SURE, YOU GOTTA CRAWL ON ALL *FOURS* FOR A COUPLE MILES...

...AND YOU SMELL LIKE A *BARN* ONCE IT'S ALL OVER...

... BUT IT DOES GET THE *JOB* DONE.

THUS ENDS ANOTHER THRILLING INSTALLMENT OF "WOLVERINE'S FACTS YOU CAN USE."

SK SS SH HH

SNIKT!

DON'T SEE WHY YOU CRITTERS GOT ANY LESS RIGHT THAN ANYBODY ELSE TO FIND YOUR OWN WAY OUTTA THIS MESS.

THERE'S ANOTHER HAZMAT SUIT IN THE CAB OF THE TRUCK.

WITH MY MUTANT HEALING FACTOR, I DON'T REALLY *NEED* IT--

--BUT I *AM* CURIOUS IF WHAT I *THINK* I'M TASTING *IS* WHAT I'M TASTING...

...*METALLIC,* ALMOST LIKE SUCKING DOWN ON *LEAD FILLINGS*-

...AND THE *INFRARED GOGGLES* ON THE SUIT WILL SHOW ME--

OH.

OH, YEAH.

THAT'D BE WHY THE WINDOWS ON THIS TRUCK HAVE BEEN PAINTED OVER WITH *LEAD*--

--WHY THOSE YO-YOS WERE ROUNDING UP ALL THE LOCAL *CUDDLIES* SO THEY COULDN'T SPREAD THEIR FUR AND DANDER--

--AND WHY I CAN TASTE *RADIOACTIVE FALLOUT* IN THE AIR.

YOU DON'T SPEND AS LONG IN *INTELLIGENCE* AS I DID WITHOUT LEARNING A LITTLE SOMETHING ABOUT *NUCLEAR INCIDENT PROTOCOL.*

THIS WOULD BE WHAT THEY CALL THE "ZONE OF ALIENATION"-- THE THIRTY KLICK RADIUS YOU GOTTA *EVACUATE* AFTER A *REACTOR EXPLOSION.*

BUT HERE *I* AM, DRIVING EVEN DEEPER *INTO* IT--INTO THE "ZONE OF PLUTONIUM"... THE *BELLY* OF THE RADIOACTIVE *BEAST.*

ЗАПРЕТНАЯ ЗОНА

AND IT AIN'T 'CAUSE I'M BORED O' *BREATHIN'.*

IT'S 'CAUSE THAT'S WHERE *KITTY PRYDE* IS.

AND IF ANYTHING... ANYTHING AT *ALL* HAPPENS TO HER IN THERE... I'LL NEVER *FORGIVE* MYSELF...

...'CAUSE THIS WHOLE THING IS *MY FLAMIN'* FAULT!

FORTY-EIGHT HOURS BEFORE:

HOW MANY TIMES I GOT TO *TELL* YOU, KIDDO?

STOP USIN' *MY* RAZOR ON *YOUR* LEG--

A-HUH-HUH-HUH-HUH-HUH-HUH!

OH! UH... I'LL JUST COME BACK LATER...

NO, LOGAN, *WAIT!* I NEED YOUR *HELP!* I DON'T KNOW WHAT TO *DO!*

PETER RASPUTIN HAS A GIRLFRIEND!!

I'M... *PRETTY* SURE HE DOESN'T, KID...

...AND I'M NOT JUST SAYING THAT BECAUSE I DON'T REALLY *CARE*...

HE *DOES!* AND I'VE MISSED MY CHANCE TO TELL HIM HOW I *FEEL* ABOUT HIM! I'M SUCH A *COWARD*...

"...I KNEW IT THE *MINUTE* I ANSWERED THE *PHONE*..."

XAVIER SCHOOL FOR GIFTED YOUNGSTERS...

ER... YES. MAY I SPEAK TO PIOTR NIKOLIEVITCH RASPUTIN, PLEASE?

"SHE HAD A *RUSSIAN* ACCENT!"

"A *CUTE* RUSSIAN ACCENT!"

COLOSSUS?

PHONE.

HELLO, THIS IS--

WHAT ARE YOU *DOING?* YOU SHOULDN'T BE CALLING ME *HERE!*

"BUT THEN HE SWITCHED TO *RUSSIAN,* AND I COULDN'T UNDERSTAND WHAT THEY WERE SAYING!"

THEY WERE MAKING PLANS TO *MEET!*

COMMIE *JERK!* I'D LIKE TO MEET HER IN A DARK ALLEY--SHE WOULDN'T BE SO *CUTE* ONCE I GOT *THROUGH* WITH HER--

WHOA! WHOA! JUMP TO *CONCLUSIONS* MUCH?

LOOK, THERE'S A SIMPLE WAY TO CLEAR THIS UP.

LET'S FOLLOW PETER TO WHEREVER HE'S GOING TONIGHT. YOU'LL SEE THERE'S NO HANKY-PANKY GOIN' ON!

YEAH, SURE.

THERE'S NOTHING GOOD ON T.V. TONIGHT.

REALLY? YOU'D SPY ON YOUR FRIEND FOR ME?

THANKS, LOGAN! *THANK YOU!*

AND SO...

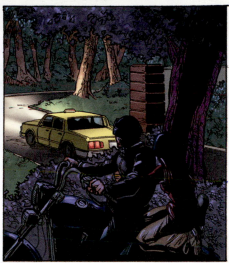

Y'KNOW, WE JUST WENT *THROUGH* THIS WHEN SIRYN VISITED.*

DON'T YOU WANNA STOP *TORTURING* YOURSELF OVER EVERY FEMALE THAT LOOKS *SIDEWAYS* AT THE RUSSKIE?

*LAST ISH. —MATCHMAKER MARK

YOU BETTER WORK UP THE COURAGE TO TELL HIM HOW Y'*FEEL*, 'CAUSE I CAN'T KEEP PLAYN' *MISS LONELYHEARTS* LIKE THIS!

I GOT A REPUTATION TO MAINTAIN!

NO, YOU'RE *RIGHT*. I'LL TELL HIM TONIGHT, I *PROMISE!*

HMMM...

CURIOUSER AND *CURIOUSER...*

<YOU SHOULD NOT HAVE CALLED ME *DIRECTLY,* LAYNIA PETROVNA! I DO NOT WISH TO GIVE THE X-MEN THE *WRONG IMPRESSION*-->*

<THE SITUATION HAS *WORSENED* SINCE WE LAST SPOKE BY ELECTRONIC MAIL, PIOTR. THERE IS NO *TIME* FOR-->

*TRANSLATED FROM *RUSSIAN.* -COMRADE PANICCIA

<IF YOU ARE SO ASHAMED OF HONORABLY SERVING OUR MOTHERLAND, PIOTR NIKOLIEVITCH...>

<...PERHAPS YOU SHOULD HAVE TAKEN BETTER PRECAUTIONS AGAINST BEING *FOLLOWED.*>

<WHAT? BUT I WAS NOT-->

<SHUT UP AND GET IN THE PLANE.>

UH-OH.

"UH-OH?!" WHAT UH-OH?!

ARE THEY KISSING?!

WWWHHIIRRRR

OKAY.

SO NOW NEW YEAR'S DAY 1975 IS THE *SECOND* WORST THING I'VE EVER WOKEN UP TO.

FASH KRASH

KRAK

BRKAK

KSSHH

BDA
BDA
BDA
BDA

HMMM.

CONSIDERING THE UNSPEAKABLE AMOUNT OF *PAIN* I'M IN...

...I'D SAY IT'LL TAKE ABOUT *TWENTY-FOUR HOURS* FOR MY HEALING FACTOR TO REPAIR THE DAMAGE.

TWENTY-FOUR HOURS TO *PAYBACK TIME.*

EIGHTEEN HOURS.

STILL *GOT* IT.

DIDN'T TAKE ME LONG TO DUMB OUT THIS PLACE WAS *CRAWLIN'* WITH PATROLS.

THEY HAD *JUST* EVACUATED THE WHOLE AREA--

-- AT THE TRAPPER'S CABIN I FOUND, THE REINDEER HIDE WAS STILL *WARM*.

IF I HADN'T BEEN SUCH A *WISE GUY* AND ENCOURAGED KITTY TO *FOLLOW* COLOSSUS, SHE WOULDN'T *BE* HERE--

--AND SHE'S *GOTTA* BE HERE! IN THE MIDDLE O' *NOWHERE* LIKE THIS, THIS IS THE ONLY FACILITY THAT WOULD HAVE AN *AIRSTRIP* FOR THAT JET TO LAND.

BUT WHERE IS *"HERE,"* EXACTLY?

THIS DOESN'T LOOK LIKE ANY *NUCLEAR POWER PLANT* I'VE EVER SEEN!

BUT WHAT *ELSE* COULD SPIT UP THIS MUCH *RADIATION?*

‹STOP! WHAT IS YOUR AUTHORIZATION TO BE HERE?›

‹I GOT YOUR AUTHORIZATION RIGHT *HERE,* COMRADE...›

WOP!

CHUD!

‹I DON'T *LIKE* THIS. THEY'VE BEEN DOWN THERE FOR *HOURS.*›

‹WHAT DO YOU EXPECT US TO DO, MIKHAIL?›

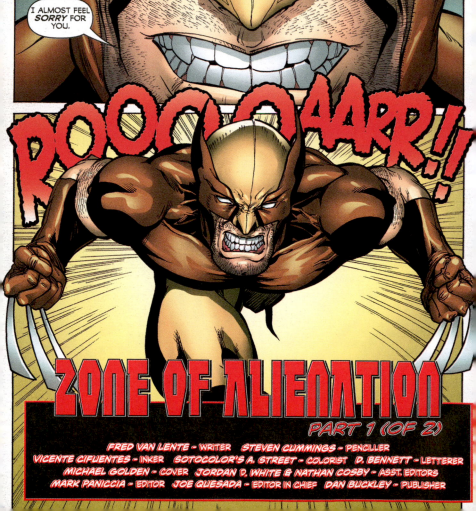

THERE'S ONLY **FOUR** OF YOU.

SNIKT! SNIKT!

I ALMOST FEEL **SORRY** FOR YOU.

ROOOOOAARR!!

ZONE OF ALIENATION

PART 1 (OF 2)

FRED VAN LENTE - WRITER   STEVEN CUMMINGS - PENCILLER

VICENTE CIFUENTES - INKER   SOTOCOLOR'S A. STREET - COLORIST   D. BENNETT - LETTERER

MICHAEL GOLDEN - COVER   JORDAN D. WHITE & NATHAN COSBY - ASST. EDITORS

MARK PANICCIA - EDITOR   JOE QUESADA - EDITOR IN CHIEF   DAN BUCKLEY - PUBLISHER

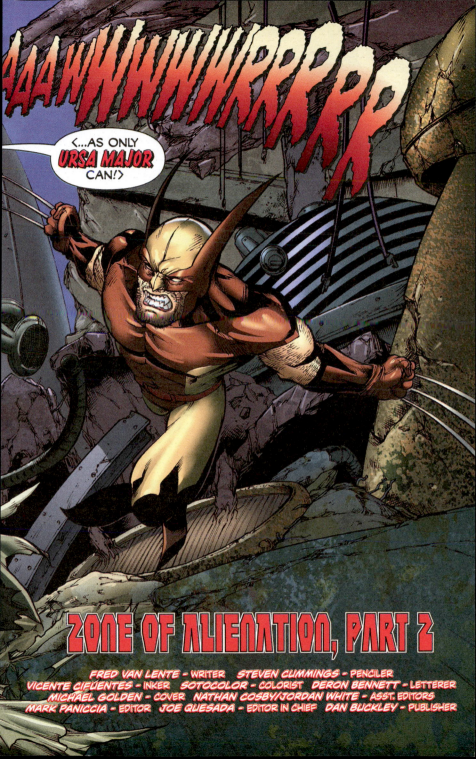

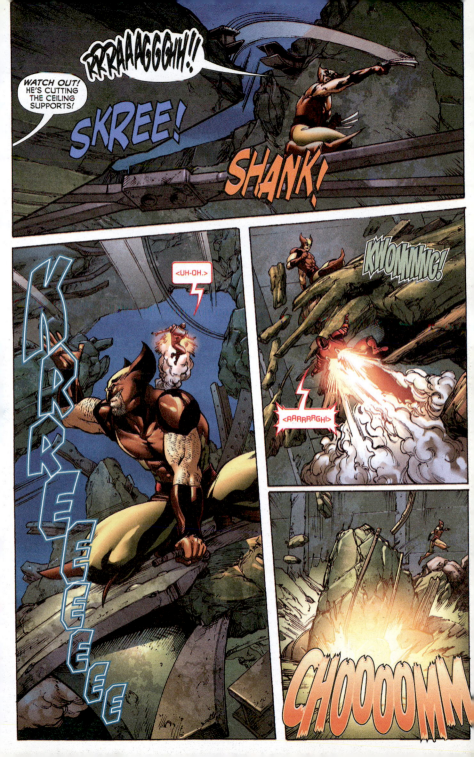

LOGAN! YOUR NAME IS *LOGAN*, YES?

YOUR FRIEND *KITTY* TOLD US THAT!

THOUGH, YES, *INITIALLY* WE TOOK HER FROM YOUR COUNTRY AGAINST HER WILL--

"ONCE WE EXPLAINED OUR PREDICAMENT TO HER AND YOUR TEAMMATE—OUR COUNTRY-MAN, *COLOSSUS*--

"BOTH AGREED TO HELP US *VOLUNTARILY!*

"WHEN THE REACTOR HERE *OVER-LOADED*, THE CORE BEGAN SINKING RIGHT THROUGH THE EARTH.

"IF THE MAGMA HITS THE *GROUNDWATER* BENEATH THE *CONCRETE FOUNDATION*–

"THE RESULTING EXPLOSION WILL BE THREE TO FIVE *MEGATONS* STRONG. NEARBY CITIES WILL BE *LEVELED* AND MUCH OF *EUROPE* RENDERED UNINHABITABLE!

"WE RECRUITED *COLOSSUS*, HOPING HIS GREAT STRENGTH AND ARMORED FORM MEANT HE COULD DEFLECT THE CORE AWAY FROM THE AQUIFER..."

"...BUT WE NOW REALIZED KITTY PRYDE COULD *PHASE* HIM EVEN FURTHER BELOW GROUND!"

AND WE ARE ALL SADDENED SHE HAS *FALLEN* IN THE ATTEMPT, BUT KNOW, LOGAN, THAT SHE WILL BE A *HERO* TO THE RUSSIAN PEOPLE FOREVER...

WHA...?

⟨WHERE-WHERE DID KITTY PRYDE *GO?!*⟩

RRRAAAAGGHHH!

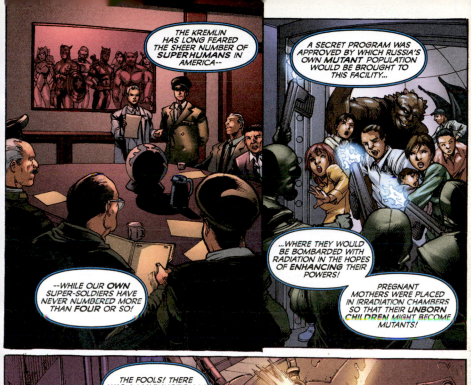

THE KREMLIN HAS LONG FEARED THE SHEER NUMBER OF **SUPERHUMANS** IN AMERICA--

A SECRET PROGRAM WAS APPROVED BY WHICH RUSSIA'S OWN **MUTANT** POPULATION WOULD BE BROUGHT TO THIS FACILITY...

...WHERE THEY WOULD BE BOMBARDED WITH RADIATION IN THE HOPES OF **ENHANCING** THEIR POWERS!

--WHILE OUR **OWN** SUPER-SOLDIERS HAVE NEVER NUMBERED MORE THAN **FOUR** OR SO!

PREGNANT MOTHERS WERE PLACED IN IRRADIATION CHAMBERS SO THAT THEIR UNBORN **CHILDREN** MIGHT BECOME MUTANTS!

THE FOOLS! THERE WAS A MALFUNCTION IN THE COOLING SYSTEM-- THE CORE **MELTED DOWN**--

THE IRRADIATION CHAMBER WAS FLOODED WITH BETA PARTICLES--

THERE WAS A FLASH OF **LIGHT**--

PERHAPS ONE OF US USED A **LATENT** POWER--

〔 185 〕

"...OUTSIDE THE ZONE OF ALIENATION!"

WE SHOULD BE *SAFE* HERE-- OR WHAT *PASSES* FOR SAFE OUTSIDE A *NUKE EXPLOSION,* ANYHOW.

THEN MY LAST ACT AS THE *DESIGNATED DRIVER* OF THIS *COLLECTIVE BODY*--

--IS TO *DE-COLLECT* IT!

OOOOFF!

‹THE SOVIET SUPER-SOLDIERS HAD NO IDEA OF THE TRUE NATURE OF THIS FACILITY.›

‹BUT NOW THAT WE *DO,* WE SWEAR WE WILL BRING THE PARTY MEMBERS WHO AUTHORIZED IT TO *JUSTICE!*›

KITTY'S DREAM

Writer: Fred Van Lente
Artist: Colleen Coover

"AT LEAST ... I *HOPE* IT'S A DREAM!"

"I'D HATE TO THINK I'VE *REALLY* BEEN 'SLEEP-PHASING!'"

La CIRQUE

"BY THE TIME I *WOKE UP*..."

?

"...I WAS IN SOME KIND OF *SUBTERRANEAN KINGDOM!*"

"I ASKED THE LITTLE *GREMLINS* WHY THEY ALL LOOKED SO *GLUM*..."

"...AND THEY SAID THEIR *BOSS* WOULDN'T LET THEM DANCE! THEY HAD TO *WORK* ALL THE TIME!"

"HE EVEN THREW THEIR *MIX TAPES* INTO SOMEPLACE CALLED *THE VALLEY OF DIAMONDS!*"

"*I* OFFERED TO GET THE TAPES FOR THEM SO THEY WOULDN'T HAVE TO LEAVE WORK!"

"IT DIDN'T EVEN REALLY TAKE ME THAT LONG!"

"THEY SEEMED REALLY GRATEFUL, TOO!"

MY X-MEN TAKE OUT TRASH ON TUES.

WHAT DO YOU THINK IT COULD **MEAN?!**

THAT YOU HAVE MANY YEARS OF EXPENSIVE THERAPY TO LOOK FORWARD TO.

BUT:

OH MY--

OH MY--

IT WASN'T A DREAM!

IT WASN'T A DREAM!!

sigh

GIRL IS JUST **TOO** EASY.

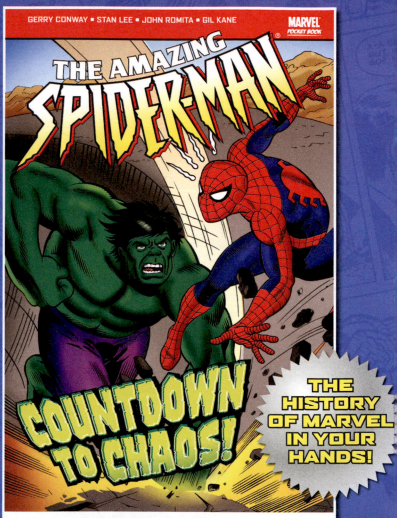